STOCKING STUMPERS

SUPER BOWL

By S. Claus

RED-LETTER PRESS, INC.
Saddle River, New Jersey

STOCKING STUMPERS - SUPER BOWL
Revised and Updated 2014
Copyright ©2013 Red-Letter Press, Inc.
ISBN-10: 1-60387-018-0
ISBN-13: 978-1-60387-018-4

Facts herein have been researched by our staff and believed
to be accurate but are made without any guarantee. The
publisher also disclaims any liability incurred by
the use of information from this book.

This publication has not been prepared, approved, or
licensed by the National Football League.
As such, this is not an official publication.

Red-Letter Press, Inc.
P.O. Box 393, Saddle River, NJ 07458
www.Red-LetterPress.com
info@Red-LetterPress.com

ACKNOWLEDGMENTS
SANTA'S SUBORDINATE CLAUSES

Compiled By:
Jeff Kreismer

Editor:
Jack Kreismer

Cover Design:
Cliff Behum

Special Mention:
Sparky Anderson Kreismer

*"If it's the ultimate game,
how come they're
playing it again next year?"*

-Duane Thomas

———————————————————

INTRODUCTION

Whether you're having a few quiet
moments to yourself or enjoying a
reunion with friends and family, Stocking
Stumpers is the perfect holiday companion.
Gather 'round the Christmas tree or simply
kick back in your easy chair while
trying out the holiday humdingers,
tailor-made tests and trivia tidbits.

Once you've had a sampling, I think you'll
agree, Stocking Stumpers is proof of the
Christmas pudding that good things do
come in small packages. Ho ho ho!

Merry Christmas!!

S. Claus

The Mantle Meter

'Tis right around Christmas
and all through the book,

There are all sorts of stumpers
everywhere that you look.

There are quizzes and seasonal tests
to take you to task,

But what are those "stocking"
questions you ask?

Well, the stockings are hung
by the chimney with care.

The more that are filled,
the tougher the bear.

And so it is that
the Mantle Meter keeps score,

Rating the stumpers,
one stocking or more.

STOCKING STUMPERS

SUPER BOWL

FIRST AND FIVE

1. Super Bowl XLI was the first to feature two African-American head coaches. Name them.

2. What New England quarterback became the first starter in Super Bowl history to fail to complete a pass?

3. For the first time in the game's history, back-to-back kickoffs were returned for touchdowns when what Giant and Raven accomplished the feat in Super Bowl XXXV?

4. When the Colts won their first Super Bowl (V), who became the first rookie head coach to claim victory in the game?

5. What Steeler became the first wide receiver to throw a touchdown pass in the Super Bowl when he hit Hines Ward for a 43-yard score?

What member of the Super Bowl XXXV champion Ravens was later diagnosed with ALS and became a source of inspiration for Baltimore's Super Bowl XLVII title?

ANSWERS

1.

Lovie Smith (Bears) and
Tony Dungy (Colts)

2.

Tony Eason, in Super Bowl XX

3.

Ron Dixon and Jermaine
Lewis, respectively

4.

Don McCafferty

5.

Antwaan Randle El (SB XL)

O.J. Brigance

SUPER BEGINNINGS

1. While the Packers-Chiefs meeting on January 15, 1967 is now referred to as "Super Bowl I", what name was the event originally given?

2. What Kansas City owner coined the phrase "Super Bowl"?

3. In their win over the Chiefs, what unlikely Packer scored the first touchdown in the history of the Super Bowl?

4. With a crowd of only two-thirds capacity, what venue hosted the first Super Bowl?

5. Who was named the MVP of the first two Super Bowls?

What Indiana alum all but sealed Super Bowl XLIV for New Orleans over the Colts with his 74-yard interception return for a TD in the fourth quarter?

ANSWERS

1.

The First AFL-NFL World
Championship Game

2.

Lamar Hunt

3.

Max McGee

4.

L.A.'s Memorial Coliseum

5.

Bart Starr, with Green Bay

Tracy Porter

RIPE FOR THE PICKING

1. Whose 56-yard "pick-six", the very first interception of his NFL career, produced the final points of Indy's 29-17 win over the Bears in Super Bowl XLI?

2. The Packers victory over the Raiders in Super Bowl II was put away when what future Hall of Famer ran back an interception 60 yards for a touchdown?

3. What Raven picked off Colin Kaepernick in Super Bowl XLVII to mark the 49ers first interception in Super Bowl history?

4. Dallas' Larry Brown was the MVP of Super Bowl XXX. Ironically, the Steelers QB he picked off twice was once the NFL's career leader in interception percentage. Who?

5. What Eagles quarterback was intercepted by Oakland linebacker Rod Martin on his first pass attempt of Super Bowl XV?

What Louisiana venue hosted three of the first nine Super Bowls before the New Orleans Superdome opened?

ANSWERS

1.

Kelvin Hayden

2.

Herb Adderley

3.

Ed Reed

4.

Neil O'Donnell

5.

Ron Jaworski

Tulane Stadium

SETTLING THE SCORE

1.
The Steelers led 2-0, the lowest halftime score in Super Bowl history, against what opponent?

2.
What was the final score of the Jets upset win over the Baltimore Colts in Super Bowl III?

3.
Who are the only two teams to score at least 50 points in a single Super Bowl?

4.
In their defeat to Green Bay, who became the first team in Super Bowl history to score 14 first quarter points and go on to lose the game?

5.
The highest point total in a losing effort in the Super Bowl is 31 points. What two NFC squads share the mark?

❄ SEASONAL STUMPER ❄

Five Golden Rings....Only one NFL player has been a member of five Super Bowl championship teams- two in San Francisco and three in Dallas. He also shares his first name with the author of *A Christmas Carol.* Name him.

ANSWERS

1.

The Vikings (Super Bowl IX)

2.

16-7

3.

The Cowboys (SB XXVII against the Bills)
and 49ers (XXIV over the Broncos)

4.

New England Patriots (SB XXXI)

5.

Cowboys (SB XIII) and 49ers (XLVII)

Seasonal Stumper Answer:

Charles Haley
(Charles Dickens is the author.)

A Simple Yes or No Will Do

1.
Has a team ever been shut out in the Super Bowl?

2.
Has the game ever gone into overtime?

3.
Does John Madden have a Super Bowl ring?

4.
Has a nine-win team ever won the Super Bowl in a 16-game season?

5.
Are the Patriots the only NFL team to ever win three titles in a four-year span?

What Steelers returner scored the first touchdown of Super Bowl XLIII and finished the game with two carries for -3 yards?

ANSWERS

1.

No

2.

No

3.

Yes – He was the head coach of
the champion Raiders (SB XI).

4.

Yes – The New York Giants
(SB XLVI) were the first.

5.

No – The Cowboys did it
first in the 1990s.

Gary Russell

QUOTE, UNQUOTE

1. Before Super Bowl I, this Chiefs cornerback promised a hard time for Packers receivers: "Two hammers to (Boyd) Dowler, one to (Carroll) Dale should be enough."

2. On playing in Super Bowl XVI as a rookie, this Bengals receiver said, "I feel like some guy who picked up a Rubik's Cube and got it right the first time."

3. Before a Dallas-Pittsburgh Super Bowl matchup, this eccentric Cowboy said Terry Bradshaw "couldn't spell 'cat' if you spotted him the 'c' and the 'a'."

4. Following their Super Bowl III loss to the Jets, this Colts tight end said, "After that game, we could have played the Girl Scouts and we wouldn't have taken it as a joke."

5. "I've been big ever since I was little." What Bear with the largest-ever Super Bowl ring size said it?

While he completed just 13 passes, what Raiders quarterback was named the MVP of Super Bowl XV?

ANSWERS

1.

Fred "The Hammer" Williamson

2.

Cris Collinsworth

3.

Thomas "Hollywood" Henderson

4.

John Mackey

5.

William "Refrigerator" Perry

Jim Plunkett

STADIA-MANIA

1. What Miami venue hosted three of the first five Super Bowls?

2. Super Bowl VIII between Minnesota and Miami was the first to be played at a venue that wasn't the home of a current NFL team. What Texas facility hosted it?

3. Super Bowl XXX between the Steelers and Cowboys would be the last to be held on a college campus. Where was it?

4. The Cowboys beat the Broncos in the first-ever indoor Super Bowl (XII), played in a city that has hosted double-digit Super Bowls. What's the venue?

5. Fact or Fib? When MetLife Stadium was named the site for Super Bowl XLVIII, it was the first time the game was granted to an outdoor venue in a cold weather environment.

With the Cowboys and 49ers, who became the first player in NFL history to win three consecutive Super Bowls?

ANSWERS

1.

The Orange Bowl (SBs II, III and V)

2.

Rice Stadium

3.

Sun Devil Stadium in Tempe, Arizona, on the campus of Arizona State University

4.

New Orleans Superdome

5.

Fact

Ken Norton, Jr.

IT'S AN HONOR

1. Four men have both a Heisman Trophy and a Super Bowl MVP to their name. How many can you come up with?

2. Two players have been named the NFL's Defensive Player of the Year and Super Bowl MVP in the same season. Can you name either?

3. What New York Giants owner is the only person ever to win both an Oscar and a Super Bowl ring?

4. In their defeat to Baltimore, what Cowboy became the first defensive player, and the first from the losing team, to be named the Super Bowl MVP?

5. What Packer became the first special teams player ever to be named Super Bowl MVP?

❄ SEASONAL STUMPER ❄

During the Ravens 2000 championship season, Brian Billick didn't want his players discussing the possibility of playing in the postseason and Super Bowl. Instead, the team used a different word when discussing "playoffs" – a "holiday" that was introduced on *Seinfeld* as a simpler alternative to the commercialized Christmas season. Do you know it?

ANSWERS

1.

Jim Plunkett, Marcus Allen,
Desmond Howard and Roger Staubach

2.

Harvey Martin (co-MVP of SB
XII) and Ray Lewis (XXXV)

3.

Steve Tisch

4.

Chuck Howley

5.

Desmond Howard (SB XXXI)

Seasonal Stumper Answer:

Festivus

WE MEET AGAIN

1. Who are the only two NFL teams to meet at least three times in the Super Bowl?

2. The Bengals lost to the 49ers in their only two Super Bowl appearances: XVI and XXIII. In which of the two games did Cincinnati hold a late fourth quarter lead?

3. The first time ever that *Monday Night Football* aired a re-match of the previous year's Super Bowl teams, the Patriots fell again to what team in 1997?

4. What two teams met ten years apart in Super Bowls (1973 and '83), each winning once?

5. Fact or Fib? While they wound up beating the Patriots both times, the Giants trailed New England after the third quarter of both Super Bowls XLII and XLVI.

Because the NFL didn't officially record the statistic at the time, whose four sacks in Super Bowl X have gone unrecognized in the record books?

ANSWERS

1.

Pittsburgh Steelers and Dallas Cowboys

2.

SB XXIII

3.

Green Bay Packers

4.

Miami Dolphins and
Washington Redskins

5.

Fact

L.C. Greenwood, with the Steelers

Either Or

1. Which 49ers quarterback holds the single-game Super Bowl record for touchdown passes with six: Joe Montana or Steve Young?

2. Who was the first team in NFL history to lose Super Bowls in four different decades: Patriots or Broncos?

3. In Super Bowl III, who became the first and only player to rush for over 100 yards while averaging over 10 yards per carry: Tom Matte or Matt Snell?

4. From 1972-80, every Super Bowl was won by a team whose starting quarterback wore the same number. Was that number 12 or 16?

5. In 1992, the Redskins defeated the Bills in the lone Super Bowl (XXVI) hosted by what venue: Minneapolis' Metrodome or California's Stanford Stadium?

Who was the first Wild Card team to win a Super Bowl?

Answers

1.

Young (SB XXIX vs. the Chargers)

2.

Patriots

3.

Baltimore's Tom Matte

4.

12

5.

The Metrodome

Oakland Raiders (SB XV)

VOWEL PLAY

Each runner below had a 100-yard game in a Super Bowl.
The first and last name is in order, but the vowels are removed.

1.

TRRLLDVS

2.

LRRYCSNK

3.

MRCSLLN

4.

MCHLPTTMN

5.

JHNRGGNS

From 1985-97, one conference won every
single Super Bowl. Was it the AFC or NFC?

ANSWERS

1.

Terrell Davis

2.

Larry Csonka

3.

Marcus Allen

4.

Michael Pittman

5.

John Riggins

NFC

THE ONE AND ONLY

1. Who is the only quarterback to be named Super Bowl MVP without throwing a touchdown in the game?

2. In their loss to the Steelers, the longest play in Super Bowl X for the Cowboys was a 34-yard TD pass from Roger Staubach to this man- the only reception of his NFL career.

3. This MVP of Super Bowl XI remains the only receiver to win the award with under 100 yards receiving.

4. When this former Colt beat Baltimore in Super Bowl III as a Jet, he became the only player ever to win an NFL, AFL and Super Bowl championship.

5. Who's the only player to have three rushing touchdowns in one Super Bowl?

❄ SEASONAL STUMPER ❄

Christmas Card Lane is located in the city where the Giants beat the Bills in one Super Bowl (XXV) and lost to the Ravens in another (XXXV). Name it.

ANSWERS

1.

Joe Namath (SB III)

2.

Percy Howard

3.

Fred Biletnikoff, with the Raiders

4.

Johnny Sample

5.

Terrell Davis, in SB XXXII

Seasonal Stumper Answer:

Tampa

TWO OF A KIND

1. The first two touchdowns of Super Bowl XLI between the Colts and Bears were scored by two players who both went to the University of Miami. Who were they?

2. What two quarterbacks are the only two players ever to win multiple NFL and Super Bowl MVPs?

3. What two NFL teams have lost all four of the Super Bowls they appeared in?

4. In their blowout loss to the Seahawks in Super Bowl XLVIII, Peyton Manning set a new record with 34 completions while which of his receivers caught a record 13 passes?

5. In their Super Bowl XXVII rout of the Bills, two Cowboys scored defensive touchdowns. Can you name either?

An odd story came out in 2013 when what Patriots owner claimed that Russian President Vladimir Putin "stole" his Super Bowl ring in 2005?

ANSWERS

1.
Devin Hester and Reggie Wayne

2.
Tom Brady and Joe Montana

3.
Vikings and Bills

4.
Demaryius Thomas

5.
Jimmie Jones and Ken Norton, Jr.

Robert Kraft

TV TIMEOUT

1. What two networks televised Super Bowl I?

2. What *Monday Night Football* announcer and Pro Football Hall of Famer was a TV analyst in the first Super Bowl?

3. NBC broadcast the Super Bowl in both 1993 and '94. Those games marked the first time that the same teams met in a Super Bowl in back-to-back years. Who were they?

4. After Super Bowl XXI, Phil Simms became the first Super Bowl MVP to utter what now-famous phrase on television?

5. Following his NFL career as a kicker, who announced double-digit Super Bowls on network TV before retiring in the 2000s?

What Chiefs linebacker and center started one Super Bowl on defense (I) and another on offense (IV)?

ANSWERS

1.

CBS and NBC

2.

Frank Gifford

3.

Dallas Cowboys and Buffalo
Bills (SBs XXVII and XXVIII)

4.

"I'm going to Disney World."

5.

Pat Summerall

E.J. Holub

First Class to Coach

1. What starter on Chicago's Super Bowl XX team earned a second ring as the Colts defensive backs coach in their win over the Bears in Super Bowl XLI?

2. What Colts Hall of Famer coached the New England Patriots to their first Super Bowl appearance (XX) in 1986?

3. Tony Dungy won a Super Bowl as both a player and a coach. His first ring came after Super Bowl XIII as a defensive back with what team?

4. What Super Bowl MVP went on to become an NFL head coach for the team he played for?

5. Before coaching a Super Bowl team in the 2000s, what quarterback led the Colts in passing yardage in each of the four seasons before Peyton Manning joined the NFL?

The starting quarterback and center on the Buccaneers 2002 Super Bowl winning squad had previously been teammates on the Vikings in the 1990s. Who were they?

Answers

1.

Leslie Frazier

2.

Raymond Berry

3.

Pittsburgh Steelers

4.

Bart Starr (MVP of SBs I and II)

5.

Jim Harbaugh

Brad Johnson (QB) and Jeff Christy (center)

JUST FOR KICKS

1. Who kicked a 32-yard field goal with five seconds left to give the Colts a 16-13 win over Dallas in Super Bowl V?

2. The first pure placekicker in the Pro Football Hall of Fame scored the first nine points of Super Bowl IV for the Chiefs. Who is he?

3. What kicker nearly cost the Dolphins their perfect season when his errant pass off a blocked field goal in Super Bowl VII was intercepted and returned for a touchdown?

4. The Ravens-49ers Super Bowl XLVII featured two kickers at opposite ends of their careers – a rookie for Baltimore and a 15-year vet for San Francisco. Name them.

5. At 54 yards, what Bills kicker set the mark for the longest field goal in Super Bowl history against the Cowboys?

❄ SEASONAL STUMPER ❄

The Giants-Patriots Super Bowl XLII featured the game's first-ever black head official. He shares his last name with the singer of the holiday hit *All I Want For Christmas Is You*. Who is he?

ANSWERS

1.

Jim O'Brien

2.

Jan Stenerud

3.

Garo Yepremian

4.

Justin Tucker and
David Akers, respectively

5.

Steve Christie (SB XXVIII)

Seasonal Stumper Answer:

Mike Carey
(Mariah Carey is the singer.)

QB QUIZ

1. In the Giants Super Bowl XXI win over the Broncos, Phil Simms set a record for completion percentage. Did he connect on over 20 of his 25 passes?

2. With Dallas and Denver, who was the first player in NFL history to start at quarterback in the Super Bowl for two different teams?

3. The second player to quarterback two different teams in a Super Bowl posts the three highest single-game passing yardage totals. Who is he?

4. Whose 119 passing yards vs. Miami (SB VI) remain the fewest of any Super Bowl MVP quarterback?

5. What two Super Bowl-winning quarterbacks share the NFL record for touchdowns without an interception in an entire postseason, with 11?

In their Super Bowl III upset, what running back provided the Jets with their only touchdown of the contest?

ANSWERS

1.

Yes- 22 (Two of the three incompletions were drops.)

2.

Craig Morton

3.

Kurt Warner, who played with the Rams and Cardinals

4.

Roger Staubach, with Dallas

5.

Joe Flacco and Joe Montana

Matt Snell

DALLAS DOMINATION

1. What Cowboys running back was the first player in NFL history to score touchdowns in back-to-back Super Bowls?

2. The Cowboys set a record that still stands by holding what opponent to just three points in Super Bowl VI?

3. What two Cowboy champs won both a college football national title and a Super Bowl as head coaches?

4. Which of the "Triplets" was *not* named a Super Bowl MVP: Emmitt Smith, Troy Aikman or Michael Irvin?

5. Fact or Fib? While the Cowboys have lost three of their eight Super Bowls, none of their defeats came by more than four points.

The Eagles Super Bowl XV defeat to the Raiders came just hours after what former Philly head coach had passed away?

ANSWERS

1.

Duane Thomas (SBs V and VI)

2.

Miami Dolphins

3.

Jimmy Johnson and Barry Switzer (They won college titles at Miami and Oklahoma, respectively.)

4.

Michael Irvin

5.

Fact

Joe Kuharich

MULTI-SPORT STARS

1. Deion Sanders is the only man to ever play in both a Super Bowl and World Series. He won titles with the Cowboys and 49ers, but came up short in 1992 with what MLB team?

2. What 1960s Packer who also played baseball with the Senators is the only other man besides Sanders to have played in an MLB game and a Super Bowl?

3. What Dallas receiver remains the only person to win an Olympic gold medal and a Super Bowl ring?

4. Who's the only man to coach a team in the Super Bowl (Vikings) and play on an NBA championship team (Minneapolis Lakers)?

5. What two Pro Bowl players from Syracuse and North Carolina are the only men to ever play on both NCAA Final Four and Super Bowl teams?

In 1989, for the first time in Super Bowl history, the game was tied at halftime. What two teams were responsible for the 3-3 stalemate?

ANSWERS

1.

Atlanta Braves

2.

Tom Brown

3.

Bob Hayes

4.

Bud Grant

5.

Donovan McNabb (Eagles) and
Julius Peppers (Panthers), respectively

49ers and Bengals (SB XXIII)

FOUR-LETTER MEN

The answers to all of these clues are four-letter last names.

1. Before Green Bay's Super Bowl XLV victory over the Steelers, only one active Packer owned a ring. He was on Pittsburgh's practice squad when they won Super Bowl XL.

2. This Bear was named the MVP of Super Bowl XX against the Patriots with 1.5 sacks and two forced fumbles.

3. He kicked the winning field goal for the Giants in their 20-19 victory over the Bills in Super Bowl XXV.

4. In Super Bowl XVI vs. the 49ers, this Bengals receiver caught 11 passes for two touchdowns.

5. This Bill had 152 yards receiving in a Super Bowl XXVII blowout loss to Dallas.

❄ SEASONAL STUMPER ❄

If you don't know the first Super Bowl that was given a Roman numeral, simply subtract the number of "Turtle Doves" from "Swans-a-Swimming" in *The Twelve Days of Christmas*. The answer is…?

ANSWERS

1.

John Kuhn

2.

Richard Dent

3.

Matt Bahr

4.

Dan Ross

5.

Andre Reed

Seasonal Stumper Answer:

Five (V)
(7 Swans-a-Swimming and 2 Turtle Doves)

It's About Time

1. What Cowboy caught two touchdown passes just 18 seconds apart in Super Bowl XXVII vs. the Bills?

2. While Chicago won, a miscue from Walter Payton in Super Bowl XX enabled the Patriots to take a quick lead just 1:19 into the action. What happened?

3. In Super Bowl XLVIII, the Seahawks provided the fastest score in the game's history, just 12 seconds in. How?

4. Three quarterbacks have thrown a game-winning touchdown in the final minute of the Super Bowl. Can you name them all?

5. Which Patriots Super Bowl title began with nearly 27 scoreless minutes and ended with five fourth quarter touchdowns?

What team was the first to win five Super Bowls?

ANSWERS

1.

Michael Irvin

2.
A Payton fumble gave the Pats great
field position and led to a 36-yard
field goal from Tony Franklin.

3.
Seattle was awarded a safety
after Denver center Manny Ramirez
snapped the ball over Peyton
Manning's head and into the end zone.

4.
Eli Manning, Joe Montana
and Ben Roethlisberger

5.
Super Bowl XXXVIII, over Carolina

San Francisco 49ers

CROSSING THE LINE

Match up each team below with the player who scored that franchise's first Super Bowl touchdown.

1. Giants   a. Keith Krepfle

2. Eagles   b. Brandon Stokley

3. Ravens   c. Rob Lytle

4. Seahawks   d. Zeke Mowatt

5. Broncos   e. Jerramy Stevens

Who did the Packers defeat in the famous Ice Bowl contest to get to Super Bowl II against the Raiders?

ANSWERS

1.

    d

2.

    a

3.

    b

4.

    e

5.

    c

Dallas Cowboys

Steel City Champs

1. What future Hall of Famer scored the Steelers first Super Bowl touchdown (SB IX), giving them all the points they would need to beat the Vikings?

2. The Steelers have twice defeated teams with 9-7 regular season records in the Super Bowl. Can you name either?

3. In the Steelers six Super Bowl victories, three wide receivers have been named the game's MVP. Who are they?

4. While they both won their Super Bowl debuts, neither Terry Bradshaw nor Ben Roethlisberger surpassed 125 yards passing. Which one also threw two interceptions?

5. Fact or Fib? The Steelers are the only team to win back-to-back Super Bowls on more than one occasion.

Four teams have never played in a Super Bowl. Who are they?

ANSWERS

1.

Franco Harris, who was the game's MVP

2.

Rams (SB XIV) and Cardinals (XLIII)

3.

Lynn Swann (SB X), Hines Ward (XL) and Santonio Holmes (XLIII)

4.

Roethlisberger

5.

Fact

Browns, Jaguars, Lions and Texans

CANTON CONUNDRUMS

1. In Dallas' Super Bowl VI win over the Dolphins, what two future Hall of Famers, known primarily from their former teams, each caught 7-yard touchdown passes?

2. Because of an injury, what all-time great was the only available Packer who didn't play in Super Bowl I?

3. As a defensive coordinator with the Giants, whose game plan from Super Bowl XXV is currently in the Pro Football Hall of Fame?

4. In what was the longest Super Bowl TD pass at the time, Johnny Unitas hit what fellow Hall of Famer for a 75-yard score in Super Bowl V?

5. Which Canton member holds the record for the most career yards rushing in the Super Bowl: Franco Harris or Emmitt Smith?

❄ SEASONAL STUMPER ❄

Dallas made history in their Super Bowl XII win over the Broncos. If you can name the biggest holiday hit song of Bing Crosby's career, you should come up with one of the two Cowboys named co-MVP and one of the three who completed a pass in the game.

ANSWERS

1.

Lance Alworth and Mike Ditka

2.

Paul Hornung

3.

Bill Belichick
(New York beat Buffalo, 20-19.)

4.

John Mackey

5.

Harris – 354 to 289

Seasonal Stumper Answer:

White Christmas is the song- Randy White was a co-MVP with Harvey Martin, and Danny White, along with Roger Staubach and Robert Newhouse, all completed passes.

GREATEST HITS

1. Ironically, this team shot their *Super Bowl Shuffle* video the day after their only loss of the 1985 season. Who are they?

2. The previous season, what eventual Super Bowl champs put out their own record in 1984?

3. What "note"-worthy name was given to the Titans dramatic 2000 postseason win over the Bills in their run to Super Bowl XXXIV, where they fell just short to the Rams?

4. In many of the game's beginning years, including the first Super Bowl, what musical acts performed at halftime?

5. At Super Bowl XXVII in 1993, the success of what music legend's halftime show led to deliberate efforts to attract top performers for the event from then on?

What Bears defensive lineman rushed for a touchdown in Super Bowl XX?

ANSWERS

1.

Chicago Bears (They lost to the
Miami Dolphins before going
on to win the Super Bowl.)

2.

San Francisco 49ers (*We Are the 49ers*)

3.

Music City Miracle

4.

Collegiate marching bands

5.

Michael Jackson

William "The Refrigerator" Perry

THE NAME GAME

1.
What Colts Super Bowl XLI
starter has the exact same name as
the Miami MVP of Super Bowl VII?

2.
When asked about the Dolphins defense
prior to Super Bowl VI, Tom Landry said
he couldn't recall any specific players.
This inspired what Miami moniker?

3.
What Steeler, whose first and last names
rhyme, recorded the Super Bowl's
first-ever safety against the Vikings?

4.
If the Pete Rozelle Trophy, given to the
Super Bowl MVP, was engraved with
the former commissioner's actual first
name, what would it be called?

5.
Long before they each won Super
Bowl titles, what three teams were
known as the Boston Braves,
Dallas Texans and Decatur Staleys?

Before Mike Ditka and Tony Dungy, who was the first man
to win a Super Bowl ring as a player and a head coach?

ANSWERS

1.
Jake Scott (The MVP was a Dolphins defensive back.)

2.
The No-Name Defense

3.
Dwight White (SB IX)

4.
The Alvin Rozelle Trophy

5.
Washington Redskins, Kansas City Chiefs and Chicago Bears, respectively

Tom Flores, with the Chiefs and Raiders, respectively

THE AGONY OF DEFEAT

1. What team was denied five Super Bowl trips when they lost all but one of their AFC Championship games in the 1970s?

2. While the Browns won only 14 games from 2008-10, they managed to take down the defending Super Bowl champs in each of those three seasons. Who were they?

3. In a play that could've tied the score, this Hall of Famer ultimately became the goat of Super Bowl XIII for Dallas by dropping a sure touchdown late in the third quarter.

4. With five, what team has lost more Super Bowls than any other?

5. He came up a yard short against the Rams in Super Bowl XXXIV, failing to reach the end zone as time ran out and leaving the Titans with a heartbreaking 23-16 defeat.

What quarterback holds the record for the most interceptions in a single Super Bowl with 5?

ANSWERS

1.

Oakland Raiders

2.

Giants, Steelers and Saints, respectively

3.

Jackie Smith

4.

Denver Broncos

5.

Kevin Dyson

Rich Gannon (SB XXXVII)

PATRIOT GAMES

1. The Patriots won the Super Bowl three out of four years in the early 2000s. Tom Brady was the MVP of two of them. Who claimed the other?

2. What was unique about the Patriots introductions before Super Bowl XXXVI?

3. In New England's upset over the Rams (SB XXXVI), who recorded the only defensive touchdown of the game?

4. What defensive player scored offensive touchdowns in back-to-back Patriots Super Bowl wins?

5. In which Patriots Super Bowl victory did Adam Vinatieri *not* make the game-winning kick: XXXVI (Rams), XXXVIII (Panthers) or XXXIX (Eagles)?

❄ SEASONAL STUMPER ❄

What 1945 Christmas Day baby became the first left-handed quarterback to win a Super Bowl (XI) when his Raiders defeated the Vikings?

ANSWERS

1.

Deion Branch

2. New England was the first Super Bowl team to be introduced to the crowd as a team, rather than individually. Others have since adopted the trend.

3.

Ty Law, with an interception return

4.

Mike Vrabel (SBs XXXVIII and XXXIX)

5.

XXXIX (Eagles)

Seasonal Stumper Answer:

Ken Stabler

WHICH DOESN'T BELONG?

1. Matt Millen was a member of three different Super Bowl winning squads. Which title team was he missing from: 49ers, Giants, Raiders or Redskins?

2. Which quarterback has *not* won at least three Super Bowls: Troy Aikman, Terry Bradshaw, Tom Brady, Joe Montana or Roger Staubach?

3. Only two receivers have had a 175-yard receiving game in the Super Bowl. Which one didn't: Muhsin Muhammad, Jerry Rice or Ricky Sanders?

4. Which Washington Redskin was *not* a Super Bowl MVP: John Riggins, Mark Rypien, Joe Theismann or Doug Williams?

5. Which player has *not* caught a Super Bowl touchdown pass from Peyton Manning: Marvin Harrison, Reggie Wayne or Pierre Garçon?

Who's the only female owner to have a Super Bowl championship team?

Answers

1.

Giants

2.

Staubach

3.

Muhammad

4.

Theismann

5.

Harrison

Georgia Frontiere, with the Rams

THE WHITE HOUSE VISIT

1. What Chicago Cubs broadcaster who later became a U.S. President is often credited with starting the White House tradition of hosting Super Bowl champs?

2. After the Ravens first Super Bowl win (XXXV), "Goose" said of the team's White House visit, "I'm a little depressed they didn't have a buffet." Who is he?

3. Why didn't the 1985 Super Bowl champion Bears make a trip to the White House after their victory?

4. "If you want to see the Steelers, invite us when we don't win the Super Bowl... (Obama) would've invited Arizona if they had won." What linebacker said it?

5. What Packers backup quarterback created controversy by wearing his old #9 Bears jersey on Green Bay's White House visit after winning Super Bowl XXXI?

Has a team ever played at a Super Bowl site which was also its home during the regular season?

ANSWERS

1.

Ronald Reagan

2.

Tony Siragusa

3. Two days after they won, the space shuttle Challenger disaster occurred, and their trip was postponed.

4.

James Harrison, after Super Bowl XLIII

5. Jim McMahon (As the answer to #2 explains, McMahon never made his first White House visit. Thus, he decided to don his Bears jersey when he had the chance.)

No

It's All Relative

1. In 2010, Joe Lombardi won the Super Bowl trophy that bears his grandfather's name as the quarterbacks coach of what NFL team?

2. These brothers each have Super Bowl rings. One was a five-year Ravens linebacker. The other led the NFL three times in interception return yardage. Who are they?

3. Can you name the first father-son QB duo to each be on a Super Bowl championship team?

4. He won a Super Bowl as a Packer (XLV) and his All-Pro older brother appeared in one as a Panther (XXXVIII). Name them.

5. When junior played in Super Bowl XXXIV with the Titans, he and his dad became the first father-son duo to each start in a Super Bowl. Who are they?

What career Raider is the only player to appear in the Super Bowl with the same team in three different decades?

ANSWERS

1.

New Orleans Saints

2.

Jamie and Darren Sharper, respectively

3.

The Grieses – Bob with the
Dolphins and Brian with the Broncos

4.

Cullen and Kris Jenkins, respectively

5.

Anthony and Tony Dorsett

Gene Upshaw (1960s, '70s and '80s)

18-1

1. Fact or Fib? In their perfect 2007 regular season, the Patriots won every game by at least seven points.

2. On the Giants final drive of the game, what Patriot dropped a potential game-sealing interception in Super Bowl XLII?

3. With just four catches during the regular season, what Giant made the miracle helmet grab that led to New York's "Super" upset over the Patriots?

4. Who was the Giants defensive coordinator when Big Blue held the record-breaking Pats to just 14 points in the game?

5. In defeat, what Patriots receiver, considered by some to be the goat of Super Bowl XLVI (also vs. New York), tied a record with 11 catches in Super Bowl XLII?

❄ SEASONAL STUMPER ❄

Only one Super Bowl site has also hosted a World Series and an NCAA Men's Final Four. It's the same venue that prevented an NFL team from being home for the holidays in 2010 when snow did severe damage to its roof. Can you name the dome?

ANSWERS

1.

Fib – In fact, the Pats beat the Giants, 38-35, in the 2007 regular season finale.

2.

Asante Samuel

3.

David Tyree

4.

Steve Spagnuolo

5.

Wes Welker

Seasonal Stumper Answer:

The Minneapolis Metrodome, home to the Vikings

BROACHING COACHING

1. Before leading the Bears, Lovie Smith made his first trip to the Super Bowl in 2001 as the defensive coordinator for what team?

2. Who was the first head coach to win four Super Bowls?

3. Who led the Colts to their first two NFL titles before coaching the Jets to their upset victory over Baltimore in Super Bowl III?

4. What two head coaches won Super Bowl titles while still in their 30s?

5. Who's the only coach to lead a team to three Super Bowl wins with three different starting quarterbacks?

What NFL stadium's address is Super Bowl Drive?

ANSWERS

1.

St. Louis Rams

2.

Chuck Noll, with the Steelers

3.

Weeb Ewbank

4.

Mike Tomlin (36, SB XLIII) and
Jon Gruden (39, SB XXXVII)

5.

Joe Gibbs, with the Redskins

The New Orleans Superdome

THE LONGEST YARD

1. The second half of Super Bowl XLVII began with the longest play in the game's history. What Raven provided it?

2. What Panther set a new Super Bowl record for the longest offensive play from scrimmage, an 85-yard touchdown reception, in Super Bowl XXXVIII?

3. What linebacker recorded the first 100-yard interception return in Super Bowl history?

4. What quarterback became the first to throw a touchdown pass in five different Super Bowls when he led his team on a record-tying 96-yard drive?

5. Who topped Marcus Allen by a yard to break the record for the longest run from scrimmage in Super Bowl history?

Before making five appearances with the Dolphins, Don Shula led another team to the Super Bowl. Who was it?

ANSWERS

1.

Jacoby Jones, with a
108-yard kickoff return TD

2.

Muhsin Muhammad, in
Carolina's loss to New England

3.

James Harrison – In Super Bowl
XLIII, Harrison picked off the
Cardinals' Kurt Warner for a TD.

4.

Tom Brady (SB XLVI)

5.

Willie Parker, who ran 75 yards
for a score in Pittsburgh's win
over Seattle in Super Bowl XL

Baltimore Colts (SB III)

LAYING IT ON THE LINE

1. What two former Vikings Pro Bowlers were Super Bowl starters on the offensive line of the 2012 champion Ravens?

2. At just under 22 years of age, what Packers offensive lineman became the youngest player ever to start in a Super Bowl (XLV)?

3. What All-Pro was the Vikings starting center in each of their four Super Bowl appearances?

4. What Hall of Fame lineman was the first man to play in a Super Bowl and later take a team to one as a head coach?

5. What Raiders Pro Bowl center mysteriously vanished before Super Bowl XXXVII and was benched for the game after resurfacing shortly beforehand?

Who was the first black
quarterback to start in a Super Bowl?

ANSWERS

1.

Matt Birk and Bryant McKinnie

2.

Bryan Bulaga

3.

Mick Tingelhoff

4.

Forrest Gregg, who played with the Packers and coached the Bengals

5.

Barret Robbins

Doug Williams, for the Redskins in Super Bowl XXII

WHAT'S WHAT?

1. What Super Bowl-related activity resulted in the NFL handing out a $100,000 fine to Mike Tice in 2005?

2. What weather-related phenomenon was unique about the Colts-Bears Super Bowl XLI?

3. What did construction worker Jeff Thomason have to do with the Eagles Super Bowl XXXIX squad?

4. Of what significance was the presence of special teamer Marty Moore, a 1994 New England draft pick, in Super Bowl XXXI?

5. What was unusual about the second half kickoff in the first Super Bowl?

❄ SEASONAL STUMPER ❄

In Super Bowl XXVII, while showboating as he neared the end zone after a fumble recovery, Leon Lett of Dallas was caught from behind just shy of the goal line and lost the ball for a Buffalo touchback. If you can remember the big gift that Ralphie wanted in *A Christmas Story*, you should come up with the Bills speedster who hit the ball from Lett in the unforgettable play.

ANSWERS

1.

He was found guilty of
organizing and profiting from a
Super Bowl ticket scalping operation.

2.

It was the first time that rain
fell throughout the game.

3.

Thomason was signed to a
one-game contract for the Super Bowl
due to Philly's injuries at tight end.

4.

Moore became the first Mr.
Irrelevant (the very last pick of the
draft) to play in a Super Bowl.

5.

NBC missed it. As a result, officials
asked the Packers to kick off for a
second time so it could be aired.

Seasonal Stumper Answer:

Don Beebe
(Ralphie wanted a Red Ryder BB Gun.)

ONE FOR THE AGES

1. Just after his 42nd birthday, what Colts kicker became the oldest player to ever participate in a Super Bowl (XLIV)?

2. What Raven was the youngest player ever to score a touchdown in a Super Bowl?

3. While he didn't throw a pass in the game, what 45-year-old QB suited up for the Falcons in their Super Bowl XXXIII loss to the Broncos?

4. Who is the youngest quarterback ever to win a Super Bowl?

5. Who's the oldest head coach to guide his team to a Super Bowl victory: Dick Vermeil or Tom Coughlin?

With just two carries for 45 yards, what Seahawks receiver ended up as the leading rusher of Super Bowl XLVIII?

ANSWERS

1.

Matt Stover

2.

Jamal Lewis, at 21 (Super Bowl XXXV)

3.

Steve DeBerg

4.

Ben Roethlisberger, at age 23, in Super Bowl XL

5.

Coughlin, at age 65 in Super Bowl XLVI over the Patriots

Percy Harvin

Over/Under

1. Was Scott Norwood's "wide right" field goal that would have won Super Bowl XXV for Buffalo vs. the Giants over or under 50 yards?

2. In the Jets upset over the Colts in Super Bowl III, how many points was Baltimore favored by: Over or under 20?

3. Jerry Rice blows away the competition for career Super Bowl receiving yards. Does he have over or under 500?

4. In Super Bowl XX, the Bears set single-game records for the most sacks and the fewest rushing yards allowed. Ironically, it was the same number. Was it over or under 10?

5. In his lone championship appearance, did Dan Marino have over or under 250 yards passing in Super Bowl XIX?

What Jet was the first player to intercept two passes in a Super Bowl?

ANSWERS

1.

Under – 47

2.

Under – 18

3.

Over – 589

4.

Under – 7

5.

Over – He had 318.

Randy Beverly (Super Bowl III)

STREAKING

1. What backup quarterback of the Bills and Chargers was a member of five consecutive losing Super Bowl teams in the 1990s?

2. With two sacks and a forced fumble in Super Bowl XLIII against Arizona, what Steeler established a new postseason record with four straight multi-sack games?

3. What team failed to score a single first half touchdown in each of its first four Super Bowl appearances?

4. En route to his second MVP, what quarterback set a new record by beginning a Super Bowl with nine consecutive completions?

5. What team ran off 24 consecutive points en route to claiming its second straight Super Bowl title in 1974?

I had a successful Jets career long before my son, Dan, won Super Bowl rings with both the Patriots and Colts. Who am I?

ANSWERS

1.
Gale Gilbert

2.
Lamarr Woodley

3.
Minnesota Vikings

4.
Eli Manning (SB XLVI)

5.
Miami Dolphins (SB VIII over the Vikings)

Joe Klecko

UNLIKELY HEROES

1. While Aaron Rodgers was the MVP of Super Bowl XLV, what Packer set career highs in the game with nine receptions for 140 yards?

2. With just three interceptions on the season, what Tampa Bay defensive back recorded two in Super Bowl XXXVII and was named the game's MVP?

3. In Super Bowl XXII, what little-known Washington runner became the first player in the game's history to surpass 200 yards rushing?

4. In their near-upset of the Steelers in Super Bowl XLIII, what Cardinal nearly matched his season total when he tied Reggie White's record with three sacks in the game?

5. What Broncos back, who had just three rushing touchdowns in his entire NFL career, scored two in Denver's win over Atlanta in Super Bowl XXXIII?

❄ SEASONAL STUMPER ❄

While the game was thrilling in itself, Super Bowl XLIII was extra special for one father and son. Dad covered the game as a Minnesota sportswriter while he watched his boy reach the end zone twice. To find their last name, fill in the blank of this 2012 festive film: *The _____ Family Christmas.*

ANSWERS

1.

Jordy Nelson

2.

Dexter Jackson

3.

Timmy Smith

4.

Darnell Dockett

5.

Howard Griffith

Seasonal Stumper Answer:

Fitzgerald (Larry Sr. and Jr., with the Cardinals)

THE END

1. Jerome Bettis went out in style, ending his playing career with a Super Bowl XL Steelers win in his hometown. Where was the game played?

2. Did John Elway's NFL career come to an end after Denver's Super Bowl win over Green Bay or Atlanta?

3. In his final NFL game, what Packer kicked four field goals in their Super Bowl II win over the Raiders?

4. The final game this Raiders Hall of Fame linebacker ever played came in a 38-9 Super Bowl XVIII drubbing of the Redskins. Who is he?

5. Fact or Fib? Ray Lewis ended both his first and final NFL seasons with Super Bowl championships.

Who scored the lone rushing touchdown in the Giants Super Bowl XLII upset over the Patriots?

ANSWERS

1.

Detroit's Ford Field

2.

Atlanta (SB XXXIII)

3.

Don Chandler

4.

Ted Hendricks

5.

Fib – He won his first ring in his fifth pro season before going out on top in 2013.

Laurence Maroney